PUBLISHED BY JONATHAN CAPE
2 4 6 8 10 9 7 5 3

FIRST PUBLISHED IN GREAT BRITAIN IN 2010 BY
JONATHAN CAPE
RANDOM HOUSE, 20 VAUXHALL BRIDGE ROAD,
LONDON SW1V 2SA

WWW.RBOOKS.CO.UK

ADDRESSES FOR COMPANIES WITHIN THE RANDOM
HOUSE GROUP LIMITED CAN BE FOUND AT:
WWW.RANDOMHOUSE.CO.UK/OFFICES.HTM

THE RANDOM HOUSE GROUP LIMITED REG. NO. 954009

A CIP CATALOGUE RECORD FOR THIS BOOK IS AVAILABLE
FROM THE BRITISH LIBRARY

ISBN 978-0-224-09673-7

THE RANDOM HOUSE GROUP LIMITED MAKES EVERY
EFFORT TO ENSURE THAT THE PAPERS USED IN ITS
BOOKS ARE MADE FROM TREES THAT HAVE BEEN LEGALLY
SOURCED FROM WELL-MANAGED AND CREDIBLY CERTIFIED
FORESTS. OUR PAPER PROCUREMENT POLICY CAN BE
FOUND AT: WWW.RANDOMHOUSE.CO.UK/PAPER.HTM

PRINTED IN CHINA

CHARLES BURNS

THE HIVE

JONATHAN CAPE
LONDON

WHAT DIDN'T I TELL HER?

WHAT PARTS OF THE STORY DID I LEAVE OUT?

I WANTED TO TELL HER EVERYTHING.

I WANTED TO TELL HER THE TRUTH.

...AND I TRIED...I REALLY DID.

HEY, ASSHOLE!

UM...
23
PLEASE.

NNKK☀ZZZZZZZ Z

23? HEARD THERE'S
SOME FUCKED UP SHIT
GOIN' ON UP THERE...

OH... OH, GOSH.

I CAN TELL YOU'RE UPSET BUT YOU SHOULD *NEVER* SAY ANYTHING LIKE THAT.! YOU'RE GOING TO BE JUST *FINE!*

I GUESS THERE WAS SOME SORT OF AN ACCIDENT BACK IN CINDY'S ROOM BUT IT HAS *NOTHING* TO DO WITH YOU!

YOU DON'T UNDERSTAND. YOU WEREN'T HERE. SHE SCREAMED ALL NIGHT AND IT GOT WORSE AND WORSE UNTIL SHE...UNTIL...

UH... DO YOU NEED ANY READING MATERIAL? I PICKED UP SOME GREAT NEW MAGAZINES IN THE LIBRARY.

HOW ABOUT THE LATEST ISSUE OF *LADIES' SPECIAL DREAM MAN?* THAT'S YOUR FAVORITE, RIGHT?

IT'S ALWAYS THE SAME HOUSE.

I SEE IT FROM A DISTANCE... AN AERIAL VIEW.

...AND THEN I FIND MYSELF INSIDE, WANDERING THE HALLS, SEARCHING FOR MY ROOM.

THAT'S ALL I WANT.

A ROOM WITH A DOOR I CAN CLOSE... A DOOR THAT LOCKS.

THE SHEETS ARE DIRTY AND THE BLANKET IS COVERED WITH STAINS AND CIGARETTE BURNS, BUT I DON'T CARE...

IT FEELS GOOD.

IT FEELS SAFE AND WARM.

...AND JUST AS I'M DRIFTING OFF, THE INTERCOM STARTS BUZZING.

UNDER THE WHITE NOISE I HEAR WHISPERING...

A DISEMBODIED VOICE TRYING TO TELL ME SOMETHING.

...TRYING TO WARN ME.

THE ROOM
RISES
AND CRACKS
OPEN...

...AND
THEN I'M
SLIDING
DOWN A
HUGE
MUDDY
SLOPE.

I'M
RIDING
IT DOWN
AND
THERE'S
NOTHING
I CAN
DO.

OH, OKAY... NOW I REMEMBER... I WAS GOING TO TELL YOU ABOUT TAKING MY DAD'S ASHES AND THROWING THEM OFF A BRIDGE.

DID I EVER TELL YOU ABOUT THAT?

YEAH, YOU DID. ACTUALLY, YOU'VE TOLD ME A COUPLE OF TIMES.

I DID? AW, WELL FUCK ME...

I TRY TO CONTROL IT... TRY TO FOCUS IN ON THE GOOD THINGS.

AHHH! IT'S SO FRUSTRATING! I'M MISSING THE LAST TWO ISSUES AND NOW I CAN'T FIGURE OUT WHY DANNY HAD TO LEAVE TOWN!

THOSE WERE THE ONLY COPIES OF *THROBBING HEART* THEY HAD IN THE LIBRARY... I LOOKED REALLY CAREFULLY.

I'M SORRY, I SOUND LIKE A REAL BITCH. IT WAS SO SWEET OF YOU TO FIND THESE FOR ME.

...BUT IT DRIVES ME *CRAZY* 'CAUSE THERE'S ALL THIS NEW, EXCITING STUFF GOING ON THAT I CAN'T FIGURE OUT.

COME HERE, I'LL SHOW YOU.

I DON'T KNOW... IT'S... IT'S AGAINST THE RULES.

DON'T BE A BIG *WIMP!* JUST SIT DOWN... NOBODY'S GONNA KNOW!

I WAKE UP WITH THE HORRORS...

IT TAKES ME A WHILE TO CALM DOWN AND FIGURE OUT WHERE I AM.

OH, GREAT... THAT'S JUST GREAT.

WHAT'S THE LAST THING I REMEMBER?

HERE'S A BUCKET. IF YOU GET SICK, USE THE BUCKET.

IF YOU THROW UP ON MY FLOOR, I'M GONNA BE PISSED.

LOOK, I'M SORRY, I...CAN'T YOU JUST SIT DOWN AND...CAN'T WE TALK ABOUT THIS FOR A SECOND?

NO, I'M DONE TALKING... I'M GOING TO BED. IF YOU WAKE UP BEFORE ME, YOU CAN LET YOURSELF OUT.

THE EVENING STARTED OUT OKAY. I BROUGHT OVER A SIX-PACK OF PABST AND A PINT OF JIM BEAM. I DID MOST OF THE DRINKING.

I ALSO DID MOST OF THE TALKING. I HAD IT IN MY HEAD THAT I WAS GOING TO TELL HER EVERYTHING... THE WHOLE STORY.

...AND I TRIED, I REALLY DID...BUT IT CAME OUT ALL WRONG.

WHAT PARTS DID I LEAVE OUT? WHAT DIDN'T I TELL HER?

I TOLD HER ABOUT THROWING MY DAD'S ASHES OFF THE BRIDGE...

...AND THE COMICS...FINDING THOSE ROMANCE COMICS WITH SARAH.

SO WHAT IS IT WITH YOU AND SARAH? EVERYTHING YOU TALK ABOUT ALWAYS COMES BACK TO HER.

AW, SHIT...YEAH, I GUESS YOU'RE RIGHT. SORRY ABOUT THAT.

THERE'S SOMETHING YOU'RE NOT TELLING ME ABOUT HER... SOMETHING IMPORTANT. I CAN HEAR IT IN YOUR VOICE.

AW, GOD...

SARAH AND I HAD SPENT MOST OF THE DAY AT SCHOOL, WORKING IN THE DARKROOM. IT WAS GREAT TO BE OUTSIDE AGAIN...OUT IN THE LIGHT OF DAY.

WE WERE WALKING BACK TO HER APARTMENT AND JUST HAPPENED TO TURN ONTO A SIDE STREET WHERE A FLEA MARKET HAD BEEN SET UP...

HEY, LOOK... COMICS. YOU LIKE COMICS, RIGHT?

SOME OLD GUY HAD A STACK OF THOSE CRAPPY ROMANCE COMICS FROM THE SIXTIES...NOTHING I'D EVER BE REMOTELY INTERESTED IN.

...BUT SARAH WAS...

GOD THESE ARE AMAZING! LOOK AT HER HAIR! MY MOM WORE HER HAIR JUST LIKE THAT!

HOW MUCH FOR THE COMICS?

THOSE? OH, HOW ABOUT A QUARTER A PIECE?

LOOK, I'VE GOT TWO BUCKS...HOW ABOUT TWO BUCKS FOR THE WHOLE STACK?

YOU DRIVE A HARD BARGAIN, YOUNG MAN...BUT I LIKE TO MAKE FOLKS HAPPY SO TWO DOLLARS IT IS.

YOU KNOW WHAT? THAT WAS REALLY SWEET OF YOU. I KNOW YOU THINK THESE ARE STUPID, BUT...

...BUT WAIT...HERE'S WHERE YOU STOP AND KISS ME....JUST LIKE THEY DO IN THE COMICS.

MY KISS WAS AWKWARD AND CLUMSY, BUT SHE MADE UP FOR IT...

SHE MADE IT FEEL PERFECT.

NICKY? NICKY?

OH WAIT, I FORGOT... SHE'S GOT BAND PRACTICE TONIGHT.

I'D BEEN TO HER APARTMENT A BUNCH OF TIMES, BUT THIS TIME IT FELT DIFFERENT.

YOU KNOW WHAT THIS MEANS? WE CAN LISTEN TO SOMETHING BESIDES PATTI SMITH...SHE'S BEEN PLAYING *RADIO ETHIOPIA* NONSTOP AND IT'S STARTING TO DRIVE ME *NUTS!*

SHE PUT ON AN ALBUM BY BRIAN ENO CALLED *BEFORE AND AFTER SCIENCE.*

...I MEAN, I HAVE NO PROBLEM WITH LOUD, ABRASIVE MUSIC, BUT SOMETIMES I JUST WANT TO ZONE OUT TO SOMETHING LIKE THIS.

WE WERE BOTH REALLY HUNGRY AND SHE MADE US A NICE DINNER...

CREAM OF MUSHROOM SOUP AND FRENCH BREAD WITH GARLIC BUTTER.

IT ALMOST SOUNDS LIKE MOVIE MUSIC...A SOUNDTRACK, LIKE MAYBE WE'RE IN A MOVIE AND THIS IS *OUR* SOUNDTRACK, YOU KNOW WHAT I MEAN?

NNN...WAIT, I...I'M SORRY. I...I DON'T KNOW WHAT I'M TALKING ABOUT.

SARAH?

GOD, I FORGOT, I *FORGOT*...THIS SONG MAKES ME TOO SAD. I CAN'T LISTEN TO THIS.

I MANAGED TO GET THE LID OFF AND SHE TOOK A COUPLE OF BIG, WHITE PILLS.

AFTER A WHILE, SHE STARTED TO CALM DOWN.

...SOME DAYS I JUST WANT TO JUMP OFF A FUCKING BRIDGE... BE DONE WITH IT ALL, BUT THEN A FEW HOURS LATER, IT ALL SLIPS AWAY AND I FEEL FINE AGAIN.

MY PARENTS HAD ME ON ALL KINDS OF MEDICATION FOR A WHILE, BUT IT KILLED EVERYTHING INSIDE OF ME.

...ALL OF MY HIGHS AND LOWS WERE GROUND DOWN TO THIS BORING, MONOTONOUS MIDDLE GROUND. I COULDN'T STAND IT.

I WAS A TOTAL ZOMBIE...I COULDN'T EVEN HAVE AN ORGASM.

LOOK, I'M SORRY ABOUT ALL THIS. YOU DON'T HAVE TO STAY IF YOU DON'T WANT TO. I'M OKAY NOW... REALLY.

BUT I WANT TO STAY. I WANT TO BE WITH YOU.

REALLY? WELL COME ON, LET'S GO LOOK AT SOME STUFF IN MY ROOM.

WHAT'S THIS ONE?

THAT'S BY LOUISE BOURGEOIS...SHE'S THIS AMAZING SCULPTOR, BUT THAT'S A DRAWING SHE DID BACK IN THE FORTIES WHEN SHE WAS RAISING A FAMILY.

IT'S CALLED FEMME MAISON. THE ENGLISH TRANSLATION WOULD BE HOUSE WOMAN OR HOUSEWIFE.

...SO YOU'VE GOT THIS BIG NAKED, ANONYMOUS WOMAN WITH A HOUSE FOR A HEAD...

...BUT WHAT'S SHE THINKING IN THERE? DOES SHE FEEL SAFE AND SECURE?

...OR DOES SHE FEEL TRAPPED?

THAT DRAWING STUCK WITH ME. FOR SOME REASON I COULDN'T GET IT OUT OF MY HEAD.

MONTHS LATER, AFTER WE'D BEEN TOGETHER FOR A WHILE, I MADE HER A LITTLE HOUSE OUT OF CARDBOARD.

I TOOK A MILLION PHOTOS OF HER WEARING THAT THING.

BUT THAT NIGHT, THAT FIRST NIGHT WITH HER... I WAS MORE THAN A LITTLE FREAKED OUT.

I DIDN'T KNOW WHAT TO SAY WHEN SHE TOLD ME, "YOU CAN STAY HERE TONIGHT BUT WE CAN'T FUCK."

THAT'S ...THAT'S FINE... I MEAN I COMPLETELY UNDERSTAND.

YOU DO? GOD, YOU'RE SO SWEET. I DON'T DESERVE ANYONE LIKE YOU.

SHE GOT READY FOR BED AND THEN CRAWLED IN NEXT TO ME, A FEW MOMENTS LATER SHE WAS SOUND ASLEEP.

BUT NOT ME. I WAS TOTALLY WIRED UP. I WANTED TO REACH OVER AND TOUCH HER SO BAD, BUT I HELD MYSELF BACK.

I THOUGHT I'D BE AWAKE FOR THE REST OF THE NIGHT BUT I GUESS I FINALLY DROPPED OFF.

SHHH!! DON'T SAY A *WORD!* HE'S RIGHT OUTSIDE THE DOOR! IF HE FINDS YOU IN HERE HE'LL *KILL* YOU!

MINUTES PASSED...

...BUT NOTHING. THERE WAS NOBODY THERE.

SARAH? COME ON, IT'S OKAY, YOU'RE HAVING A BAD DREAM OR SOMETHING.

I... I DIDN'T WANT TO DO THIS...I DIDN'T WANT THIS TO HAPPEN AGAIN.

I'M NOT SURE I UNDERSTAND, BUT... BUT DON'T WORRY, I'LL TAKE CARE OF YOU...I WON'T LET ANYTHING HAPPEN TO YOU.

I THOUGHT MAYBE THINGS COULD BE DIFFERENT THIS TIME, BUT I WAS WRONG.

I WOKE UP SLOWLY.

I COULDN'T SEEM TO PULL MYSELF OUT OF SLEEP.

IT WAS NICE TO HOLD ON TO THAT SLEEPY FEELING... TO JUST LIE THERE QUIETLY AND WATCH SARAH READ HER COMIC BOOK.

HER DARK HAIR AND HER PALE SKIN LOOKED SO BEAUTIFUL IN THE MORNING LIGHT.

...BUT AS I CONTINUED TO LOOK, I NOTICED A FAINT NETWORK OF THIN WHITE SCARS.

HEY, SLEEPY HEAD... FINALLY DECIDE TO WAKE UP?

SCOOT OVER HERE... YOU'VE GOT TO CHECK THIS OUT. THESE STORIES ARE TOTALLY *INSANE!*

LISTEN TO THIS: "OUR LIPS TOUCHED, LINGERING BRIEFLY WITH TANTALIZING SWEETNESS... AND THEN LOCKED IN A CARESS THAT MADE THE SKY LIGHT UP AND TURN DIZZILY TOPSY-TURVY!"

...HERE'S ANOTHER ONE: "IT WAS A LONG TREMULOUS KISS FILLED WITH THE YEARNING HUNGER OF OUR UNSPOKEN LOVE."

"NOW WITH MY LIPS TINGLING FROM HIS KISS, I KNEW THAT I COULD NEVER LET HIM OUT OF MY LIFE...NOT AT ANY COST..."

MMM...MAKES ME FEEL ALL FUNNY INSIDE...THINK YOU CAN MAKE MY LIPS TINGLE LIKE THAT?

GEE, I DON'T KNOW... I'M NOT SURE I'VE HAD ENOUGH PRACTICE.

YEAH?? WELL WHAT'S STOPPING YOU?

I COULD HEAR FOOTSTEPS IN THE HALL...DISTANT MUSIC...

AW, SHIT! SORRY, I THOUGHT YOU WERE ALONE.

I WAS GONNA TELL YOU THAT ROY AND I MADE SOME BREAKFAST, BUT...

SOUNDS GREAT! WE'LL BE THERE IN JUST A MINUTE.

IT'S NO BIG DEAL. TAKE YOUR TIME.

THAT WAS THE START OF IT.

WALKING HOME LATER THAT MORNING, THE SKY WAS IMPOSSIBLY BRIGHT AND BLUE.

I REMEMBER THINKING, "THIS IS IT... THIS IS WHAT I'VE BEEN WAITING FOR MY ENTIRE LIFE."

...AND FOR A WHILE THERE EVERYTHING WAS PERFECT.

EVERYTHING WAS BRIGHT AND FUN AND NEW.

I'M GOING TO GO BACK AND GET READY... SEE YOU IN A FEW MINUTES.

ROY WAS NICKY'S BOYFRIEND...AND SHE WAS THE ONE WHO CAME UP WITH THAT STUPID NAME.

ROY WANTED TO CALL THE BAND "ANIMAL BYPRODUCTS" BUT HE EVENTUALLY GAVE IN TO NICKY.

HE WAS THE ONLY ONE WITH ANY REAL TALENT...EVEN THOUGH IT WAS HARD TO TELL IN THOSE DAYS.

AT THAT POINT THEY'D ONLY PLAYED A COUPLE OF SHOWS AND THEY WERE STILL PRETTY AWFUL.

...BUT I DIDN'T CARE. NONE OF THAT MATTERED TO ME.

I WASN'T REALLY EVEN PART OF THE BAND.

ALL I WANTED WAS A CHANCE TO GO OUT THERE AND GET ON STAGE.

I DIDN'T BOTHER TO INTRODUCE MYSELF.

I JUST TURNED ON MY CASSETTE DECK AND LAUNCHED RIGHT IN.

JUHH! UNNNN! AA AA*

PETAL EFFECTS IN BLUE EYES SWOLLEN THE SAME MOUTH ON A WHISPER A HISS

ROY HAD HELPED ME PUT THE TAPE TOGETHER...

EXPLOSIONS, PORNO SEX NOISE, BUZZING INSECTS...

ZZZZ

PINT OF SOMETHING BEAUTIFUL DISEASE HIS DESERTED COCK WINDS OF SICKNESS

THE AUDIENCE WAS TOTALLY INTO IT... ALL OF THEIR EYES WERE ON ME. I WAS RELAXED... IN CONTROL.

DAYS GROWING LONG A WORTHY VESSEL SILENT AND SHAKING ON PRENATAL FLESH

MMM

OCCASIONALLY I'D GLANCE UP AND SEE SARAH OUT THERE WITH A SMILE ON HER FACE.

CUKKK

BULB OF ORGASM VIRUS WOULD INVITE THE PREVIOUS TENANT COLD AS LIQUID AIR

THE SKY LIT UP BY IRIDESCENT LAGOON INTO FOAM MATTRESS INSECT PLEASURES

OOHH

...AND IT WASN'T A FAKE SMILE.

IT WAS THE REAL THING.

I WOULD HAVE DONE ANYTHING TO KEEP THAT SMILE ON HER FACE.

...BUT I GUESS THINGS DON'T ALWAYS WORK OUT THE WAY THEY'RE SUPPOSED TO.

THAT... WHO *IS* THAT?

IT'S *ME*, DAD... IT'S DOUG.

NO, NO... THAT THING ON YOUR SHIRT... WHO *IS* THAT?

OH, THIS... IT'S... IT'S A CHARACTER I SORT OF MADE UP AND...

AHH! UNN...

AHHH... OHH...

ARE YOU OKAY? CAN I ...YOU WANT A GLASS OF WATER, OR...

UNN... NO THANKS, DOUGY... I ...I THINK I'M DONE WITH ALL OF THAT.

I THINK I'VE ALREADY HAD MY LAST GLASS OF WATER,

THERE'S ALWAYS A LAST EVERYTHING, RIGHT?

RIGHT.

GOSH, I... I CAN NEVER DECIDE WHAT TO CHOOSE.

COME ON, FUCK-FACE! WE DON'T GOT ALL DAY!

MMM... LOOKS MIGHTY TASTY.

HEY, HEY! I THOUGHT I MIGHT FIND YOU HERE!

LOOK, I HATE TO SAY IT BUT I'VE GOT A FEW UNANTICIPATED EXPENSES THIS WEEK AND I'M GONNA HAVE TO HIT YOU UP FOR AN ADVANCE.

AN ADVANCE? DIDN'T I JUST GIVE YOU AN ADVANCE A COUPLE OF DAYS AGO?

I HAD THIS IDEA THAT WE'D GET CLOSER IF I SHOWED HER THE HOUSE I'D GROWN UP IN.

LET ME TRY MOVING THIS LAMP...IT'S STILL A LITTLE TOO BRIGHT.

THERE... THAT'S BETTER.

SO WHAT SHOULD I DO? HOW DO YOU WANT ME TO POSE?

...AND MY MOM WAS OUT OF TOWN SO I GUESS THAT WAS A BIG PART OF IT TOO.

JUST THINK ABOUT YOUR DAD...WHAT WOULD *HE* DO?

I, UH...I GUESS HE'D REACH FOR A SMOKE AND...

AW, *SHIT!* THERE'S STILL A BUNCH OF STUFF IN HIS POCKETS!

YEAH? LET'S SEE! PULL IT OUT!

IT WAS SARAH'S IDEA TO TAKE PHOTOS DOWN IN MY DAD'S OFFICE...

GOD, WHAT A *BABE!* IS THAT YOUR MOM?

THE WHOLE THING SORT OF CREEPED ME OUT, BUT I DIDN'T SAY ANYTHING.

NO, THAT'S... I DON'T KNOW WHO THAT IS.

I SAT BACK AND WATCHED AS SHE WENT THROUGH MY DAD'S DESK AND ALL OF HIS FILE CABINETS.

SHE WAS *SO* WIRED AND EXCITED... IT WAS LIKE SHE WAS ON A TREASURE HUNT OR SOMETHING.

I'D READ ABOUT OPIATES, BUT I'D NEVER TRIED THEM BEFORE.

AFTER A WHILE I FELT A DEEP WARMTH ENTER ME...STARTING IN MY STOMACH AND THEN SLOWLY RISING UP TO MY CHEST.

I REMEMBER THINKING TO MYSELF, "WHY CAN'T I FEEL LIKE THIS ALL THE TIME?"

SITTING THERE WITH SARAH, I REALIZED HOW NERVOUS I'D BEEN ALL DAY...FROM THE MOMENT WE'D STEPPED INTO MY PARENTS' HOUSE.

HE MUST BE JUST ABOUT YOUR AGE IN THIS ONE...

...BUT THE WARMTH RISING UP IN ME HAD PUSHED AWAY ALL OF THOSE NAGGING, ANXIOUS FEELINGS. I'D BEEN CUT FREE ...UNTETHERED.

EXCEPT FOR THE RED HAIR, HE LOOKS A LOT LIKE YOU.

YEAH, YEAH, I GUESS SO.

THE PHOTOS WERE SIMPLE AND STRAIGHTFORWARD...A BRIEF HISTORY OF MY FATHER'S LIFE.

A LIFE FILLED WITH FRIENDS, FAMILY, PETS, CARS, VACATIONS, BIRTHDAY PARTIES...

HE LOOKED SO YOUNG AND NAIVE... AND HOPEFUL. SOMEONE WITH A WHOLE LIFE TO LOOK FORWARD TO.

...SOMEONE I COULD BARELY RECOGNIZE.

BY THE TIME I CAME ALONG, HE'D SETTLED INTO THE GOOD LIFE... A WIFE, A JOB, A NICE HOME.

HE SEEMED LIKE ALL THE OTHER DADS OUT THERE...WORKING HARD, TRYING TO DO THE RIGHT THING.

...BUT AS I GOT OLDER, SOMETHING SHIFTED...HE SLOWLY STARTED TO RETREAT...DRIFT AWAY.

BY THE TIME I WAS IN HIGH SCHOOL HE'D QUIT HIS JOB AT THE BANK AND STARTED WORKING AT HOME.

IT WAS WEIRD HAVING HIM HOME ALL DAY... DOWN THERE IN HIS LITTLE SMOKE-FILLED OFFICE.

YOU MIND CHANGING THE CHANNEL? I'M FED UP WITH THIS SHIT.

HOW ABOUT CHANNEL TWO? LOOKS LIKE AN OLD MOVIE OR SOMETHING.

NAW... KEEP GOING.

ABOUT A WEEK AFTER WE GOT BACK TO SCHOOL, SARAH SHOWED ME THE PRINTS SHE'D MADE.

LOOKING AT THEM MADE ME FEEL AWFUL...

...MADE ME FEEL LIKE SHIT.

SO WHAT DO YOU THINK?

UH...THEY'RE NICELY PRINTED AND ALL BUT I... I DON'T KNOW.

YOU DON'T *KNOW?* WHAT'S *THAT* SUPPOSED TO MEAN? I THOUGHT I GOT SOME REALLY GREAT SHOTS OF YOU.

MAYBE I'M MISSING SOMETHING BUT I DON'T LOOK ALL "SWEET AND INNOCENT" LIKE YOU WERE TELLING ME...I LOOK LIKE A FUCKING *IDIOT!*

...AND I CAN'T BELIEVE YOU WENT THROUGH ALL MY DAD'S SHIT AND MADE ME PUT ON HIS FUCKING BATHROBE AND...

WAIT. I DIDN'T *MAKE* YOU DO ANYTHING. YOU COULD HAVE TOLD ME TO STOP AND IT WOULD HAVE ENDED RIGHT THERE.

MAYBE I SHOULD HAVE TAKEN PHOTOS OF YOU WEARING YOUR LITTLE MASK...MAYBE *THAT* WOULD HAVE MADE YOU HAPPY.

THAT WAS OUR FIRST REAL ARGUMENT. I MADE A HALF-HEARTED ATTEMPT TO APOLOGIZE BUT IT DIDN'T GO OVER VERY WELL.

SARAH TOOK A SLEEPING PILL AND WENT TO BED WHILE I STAYED UP AND SORTED THROUGH THE BOX OF POLAROIDS I'D BROUGHT OVER.

DEEP DOWN INSIDE I KNEW SHE WAS RIGHT...I WAS THE ONE WHO ALWAYS PLAYED IT SAFE.

I'D BEEN TAKING THE SAME BORING SELF-PORTRAITS FOR YEARS AND YEARS.

ONCE YOU GOT PAST THE GIMMICK OF ME WEARING MY STUPID LITTLE MASK, THERE WASN'T MUCH THERE.

JESUS...I'M NEVER GONNA DO ANYTHING WORTH SHIT.

I'M NEVER GOING ANYWHERE.

BZZZZ

I KNEW I SHOULDN'T ANSWER THE DOOR, BUT I DIDN'T WANT SARAH TO WAKE UP.

I THOUGHT MAYBE NICKY HAD LOST HER KEYS OR SOMETHING.

YEAH? WHO'S THERE?

I THOUGHT WRONG.

WHY AREN'T YOU FUCKING? YOU SHOULD BE FUCKING.

SHE'S A GOOD FUCK ISN'T SHE?

LOOK...I DON'T KNOW WHO YOU ARE BUT I... IF YOU DON'T GO I'M CALLING THE COPS.

LET ME ASK YOU A QUESTION...HAVE YOU EVER HAD ANYONE STICK A KNIFE UP YOUR ASS?

ANY HALFWAY INTELLIGENT PERSON WOULD HAVE FIGURED IT OUT... TAKEN HIS THREATS SERIOUSLY.

...BUT WHAT DID I KNOW? I WAS YOUNG AND DUMB. I WAS IN LOVE AND THAT WAS ALL THAT MATTERED.

AW, *SHIT!* THESE ARE THE ONES I'VE BEEN *LOOKING* FOR.

SARAH'S GOING TO *LOVE* THESE.

BUT AS I LOOK I REALIZE THE IMAGE WON'T HOLD...

IT HAS A LIFE OF ITS OWN.

THERE'S NOTHING I CAN DO ABOUT IT.

NOTHING TO HOLD ON TO.

IT TAKES ABOUT HALF AN HOUR TO GET THERE, BUT IT'LL BE WORTH IT... THIS STORE'S GOT EVERYTHING.

SO WHAT WAS THE NAME OF THAT MAGAZINE YOU WERE LOOKING FOR?

THROBBING HEART, NUMBERS 39 AND 40.

WAIT! THAT'S A ROMANCE BOOK! ONLY GIRLS READ THAT SHIT!

I KNOW. I ALREADY TOLD YOU, IT'S NOT FOR ME, IT'S FOR SUZY.

SUZY? YOU MEAN ONE OF THOSE BREEDERS YOU WORK FOR? YOU GOTTA BE KIDDING ME!

SHE'S REALLY NICE. I THINK SHE LIKES ME.

BUT SHE'S A BREEDER! THEY'RE NOT LIKE REGULAR GIRLS...I MEAN, SHE'S GOT DIFFERENT EQUIPMENT!

IT DOESN'T MATTER. I JUST WANT TO MAKE HER HAPPY.